my first 200 words color and learn

Inside are over 200 words to learn through four different coloring activities!

Coloring
Straightforward coloring that encourages hand/eye co-ordination and gives a free reign to imagination.

Follow-the-dot coloring
Learning about colors and following simple instructions.

Find and color
Finding a range of large and small objects in a familiar setting to encourage concentration.

Color to copy
Copying the colors from a smaller version of the illustration to encourage attention to detail.

Plus find the cute puppy in each of the six color scenes.

building block

toy box

book

xylophone

kite

jump rope

ball

drum

paintbrush

paint

pencil

Storybooks

Look for these pictures in the scene below and then color them in when you've found them. Can you find the cute puppy?

frog

wishing well

witch

unicorn

princess

fairy

castle

wand

knight

giant

horse

dragon

scarf

gloves

umbrella

sunglasses

hedge

flower

boots

pot

snail

wheelbarrow

bench

slide

helmet

swing

roller
skate

scooter

clown

chef

builder

ballerina

At school

Look for these pictures in the scene below and then color them in when you've found them. Can you find the cute puppy?

pencil

computer

book

sandpit

ruler

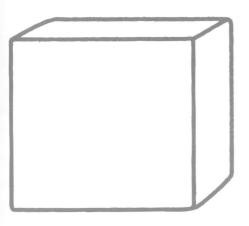

building brick

scissors

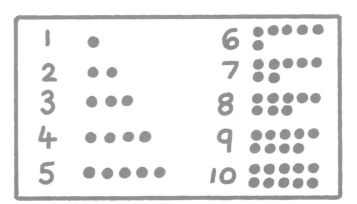

lunch box

calendar

1	•	6	•••••
2	••	7	••••
3	•••	8	•••••
4	••••	9	•••••
5	•••••	10	•••••

numbers

roof

curtain

window

door

sail

boat

fins

inner tube

beach ball

starfish

seagull

shell

beach chair

bucket

flag

sandcastle

crab

cereal

jelly

yogurt

cup cake

cow

fence

goose

reed

lily pad

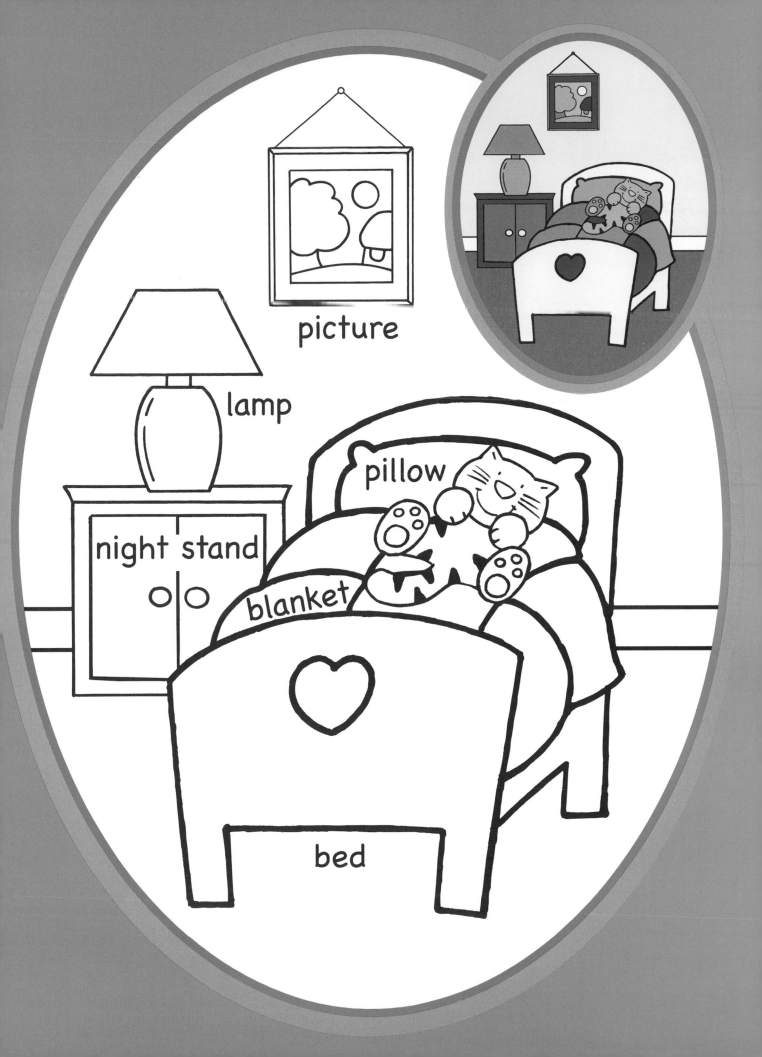

picture

lamp

night stand

pillow

blanket

bed

In the garden

Look for these pictures in the scene below and then color them in when you've found them. Can you find the cute puppy?

shed

tree

snail

watering can

bird

bush

bee

fork

flower

shovel

bird house

plant pot

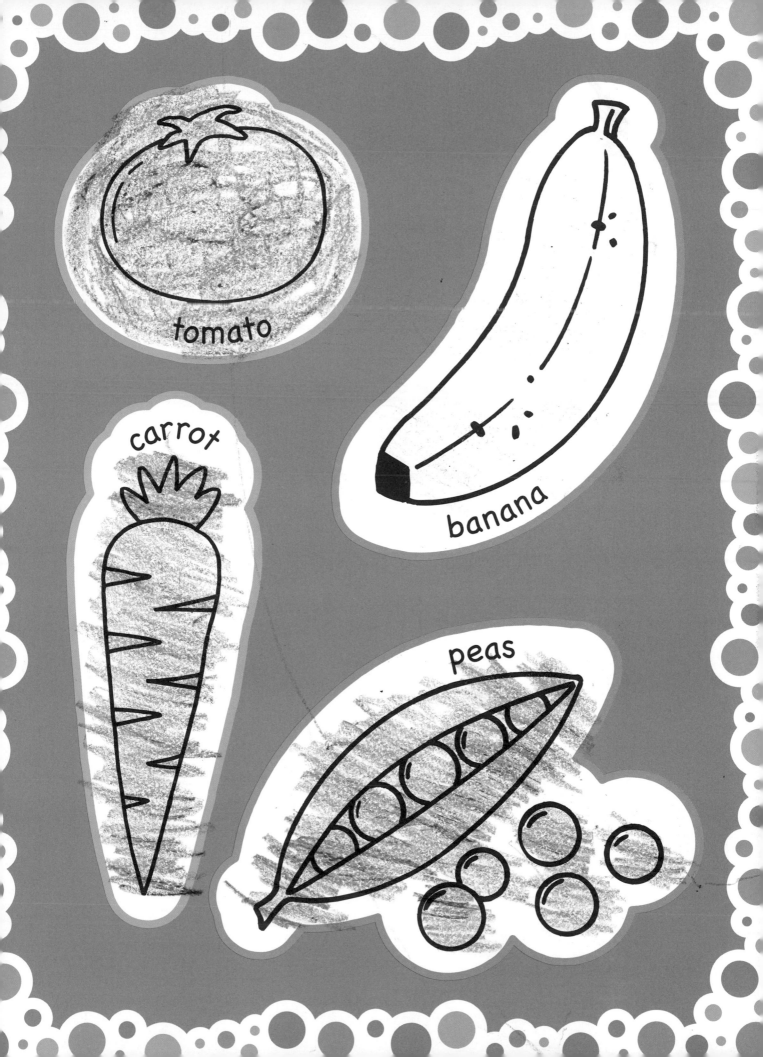

tomato

banana

carrot

peas

easel

table

paint

snow

snowman

squirrel

snowball

giraffe

camel

lion

kangaroo

At the supermarket

Look for these pictures in the scene below and then color them in when you've found them. Can you find the cute puppy?

attendant

baker

cash register

shopping basket

butcher

shopping cart

bag

bottle

purse

can

trumpet

drum

hot-air balloon

rainbow

rain

trampoline

bowling ball

board game

merry-go-round

party hat

candle

birthday cake

sandwich

cookie

driver

train

track

In the kitchen

Look for these pictures in the scene below and then color them in when you've found them. Can you find the cute puppy?

grater

mixer

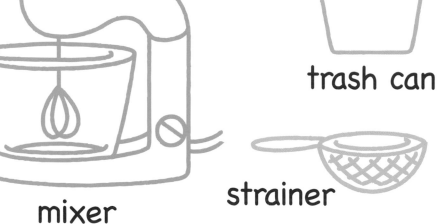
trash can

strainer

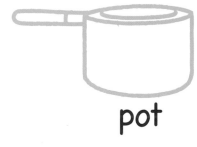
pot

cutting board

clock

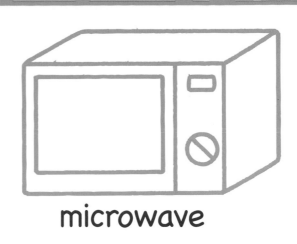

microwave

spoon

oven

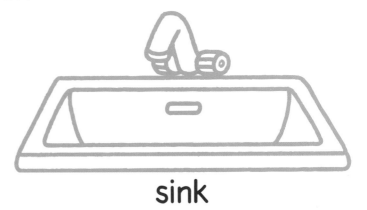

sink

monkey

parrot

elephant

hippo

house

car

bus

church

path

dog

tricycle

wheel

kite

rocking horse

teddy bear

doll

In the bathroom

Look for these pictures in the scene below and then color them in when you've found them. Can you find the cute puppy?

scale

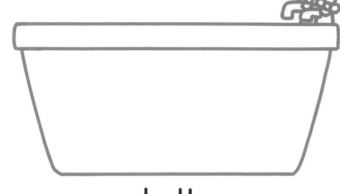
bath

towel

sink

toilet
paper

cabinet

rubber
duck

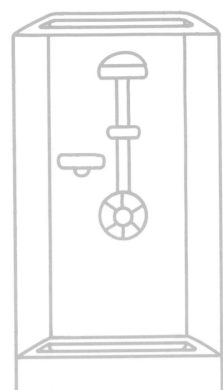

shower

toilet

mirror

faucet

cloud

hill

picnic

ship

mixer truck

helicopter

dump truck

Further Information

Here are some tips for ensuring your child gets the most in terms of fun and learning out of **my first 200 words color and learn.**

Reading and words

Talk about the familiar scenes and settings and ask your child to pick out the objects he or she recognizes. Then encourage your child to make the link between a word and its image by:

- covering over the image and asking your child to sound out first and last letter sounds
- seeing if your child can phonetically spell out the simpler words—C A T
- showing him or her the image and letting your child "read" the label when he or she recognizes the image
- encouraging your child to think of other words he or she knows beginning with the same letter sounds
- finding other words on the page beginning with the same letter.

Coloring

Coloring is fun, and also encourages your child's hand/eye co-ordination, which is a crucial first step in letter formation.

Your child is encouraged to give his or her creativity a free reign in the straightforward coloring activities and to match colors in the color-to-copy and follow-the-dot coloring activities.

Find and color

Included in the book are six busy, lively color scenes that your child can enjoy talking about. Fire up your child's imagination by asking what he or she thinks is happening in the picture. For example, "What plants are growing in the garden?", "What are the people in the supermarket going to buy?"

Then focus your child's attention on the selection of objects to be found in the main image, which is a guaranteed way of encouraging concentration! And don't forget to ask your child to find the cute puppy who appears somewhere in each of the six scenes.